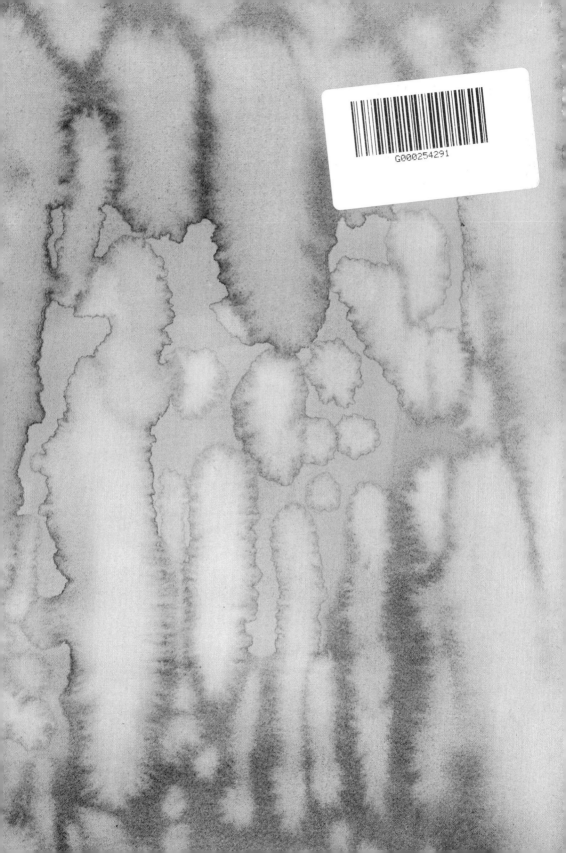

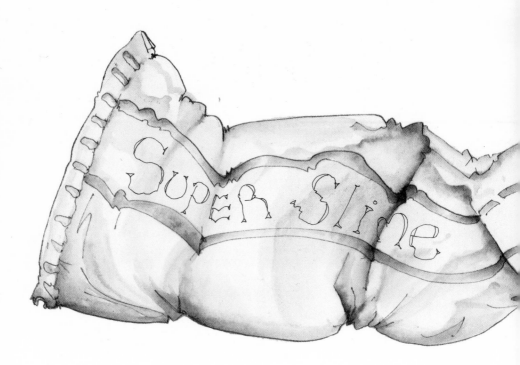

THE SLIMY BOOK

Babette Cole

JONATHAN CAPE
THIRTY-TWO BEDFORD SQUARE LONDON

Sticky, sludgy, slippy slime,

the sloppy, ploppy, creepy kind.

Slime in
my
pocket,

in my
shoe.

Is it
custard?

Is it glue?

Hello, slimy squids,

slugs,

snails,

and
slippery
toads
in slimy
pails.

Slimy worms on the lawn,

newts
from
ponds,

and green
frog-spawn.

Octopi
with slimy
limbs

eat little fish with slimy fins!

Fat ladies rub slime on their skin,

hoping it will make them thin!

People with no teeth, it's said,

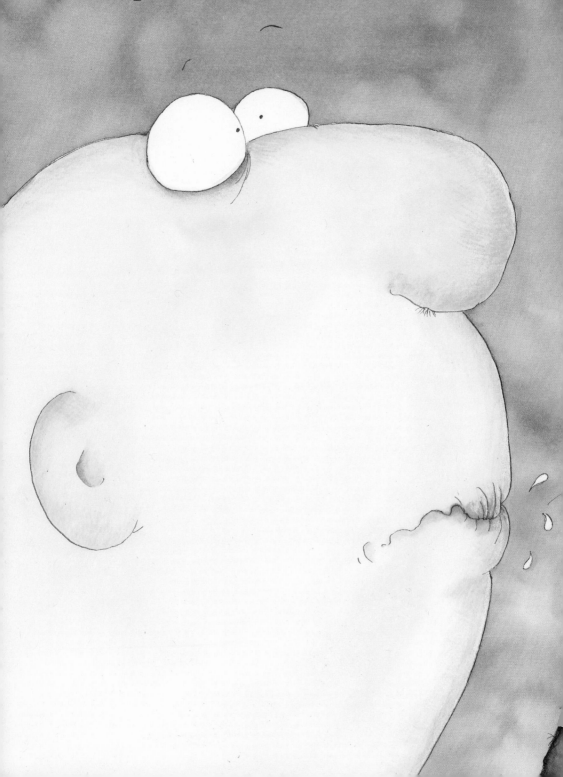

can't eat a slimy pickled egg!

Slime loves dribbling down the drain,
and blocking all the pipes again!

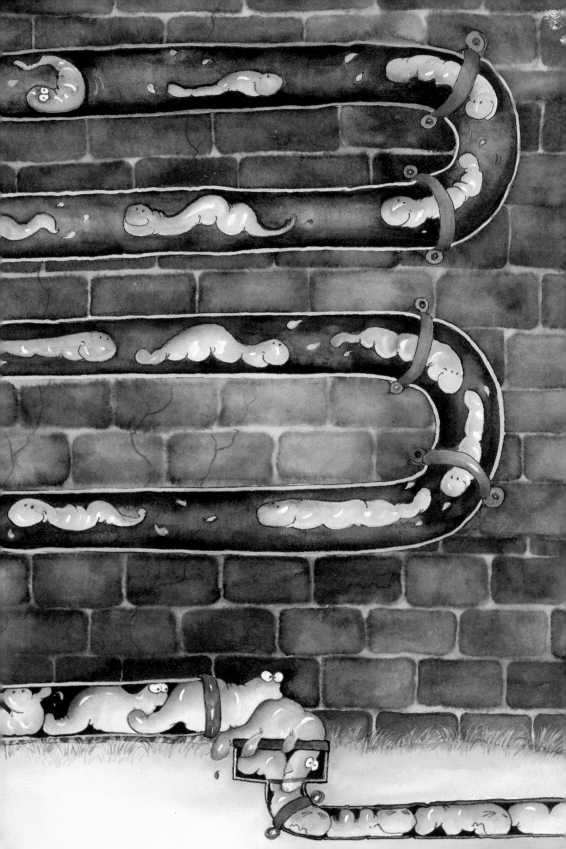

Maybe it's lurking in the loo.

Careful! It could pounce on you!

I wonder how it really feels,
slurping slimy
jellied eels…

Here's someone having slime for tea,
I hope they never invite me!

Blimey! Slimy, oodles noodles,

slimy sausages for poodles…

Slimy butter,

slimy jelly,

slimy baked beans,

bulging belly!

I should have listened
to my Mum,

who said, "Don't chew
that bubblegum!
It is the slimy
kind that clings…

to your nose and other things!"

And I wish
I hadn't tried
those horrid sweets
with slime inside!

With all the slime inside this book,
strange creatures came to have a look,

slimy green things straight from Mars,
and planets far beyond the stars,

they ate it up and left behind
trails of yellow glistening slime!

Goodbye, you slimy things
I've seen…

I'm glad that you
were all a dream!

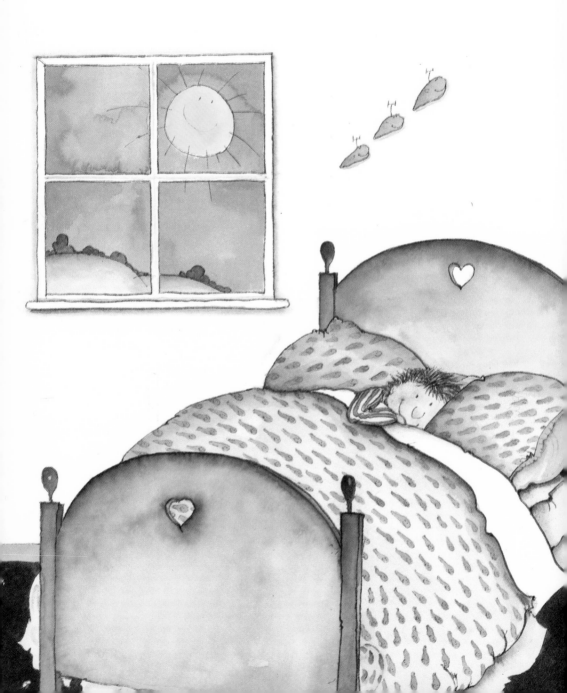

First published 1985
Copyright © Babette Cole 1985
Jonathan Cape Ltd, 32 Bedford Square, London WC1B 3EL

British Library Cataloguing in Publication Data

Cole, Babette
The slimy book.
I. Title
823'.914[J]   PZ7

ISBN 0-224-02843-X

Printed in Great Britain by Blantyre Printing Ltd,
Blantyre, Glasgow.

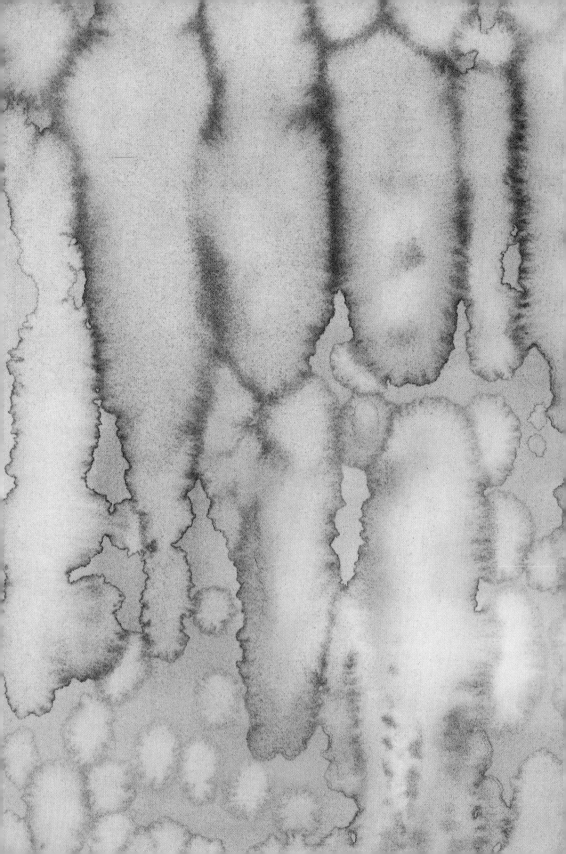